Shamu®
and the
Adventurous
Seal Pup

Written by Mark Shulman
Illustrated by Michael Kilfoy

A SeaWorld® Publication

A Dedication to Children:

Exercise your creativity, Stretch your imagination, Run to your dreams.

SeaWorld.
ADVENTURE PARKS

Orlando, San Antonio & San Diego

Text copyright ©2002 Mark Shulman   Illustrations copyright ©2002 Michael Kilfoy
Photographic and Illustration resources copyright ©2002 SeaWorld and Michael Kilfoy

Shamu is a registered trademark of SeaWorld, Inc.
©2002 SeaWorld, Inc. All Rights Reserved.
For information about permission to reproduce select images from this book,
write to: Permissions, Busch Entertainment Corporation
231 S. Bemiston, Ste. 600, Clayton, Missouri 63105
No part of this publication may be reproduced or transmitted in any form
or by any means without permission in writing from the publisher.
Published by Busch Entertainment Corporation.

This book was produced by Momentum, in collaboration with Aspen Marketing.
Anne Oller, Creative Director

Special thanks to the SeaWorld Photographic Resources Department for the
photographic images supplied to create this book; to John Sartorius and Colleen Ide;
and to the SeaWorld Education Department for their marine animal expertise.

Printed in the United States of America

I'm Shamu the whale. It's bedtime at SeaWorld,
and Baby Shamu is one tired whale calf.

Everyone is getting ready to sleep.
The polar bear mama helps her young cub lie down and tuck in.

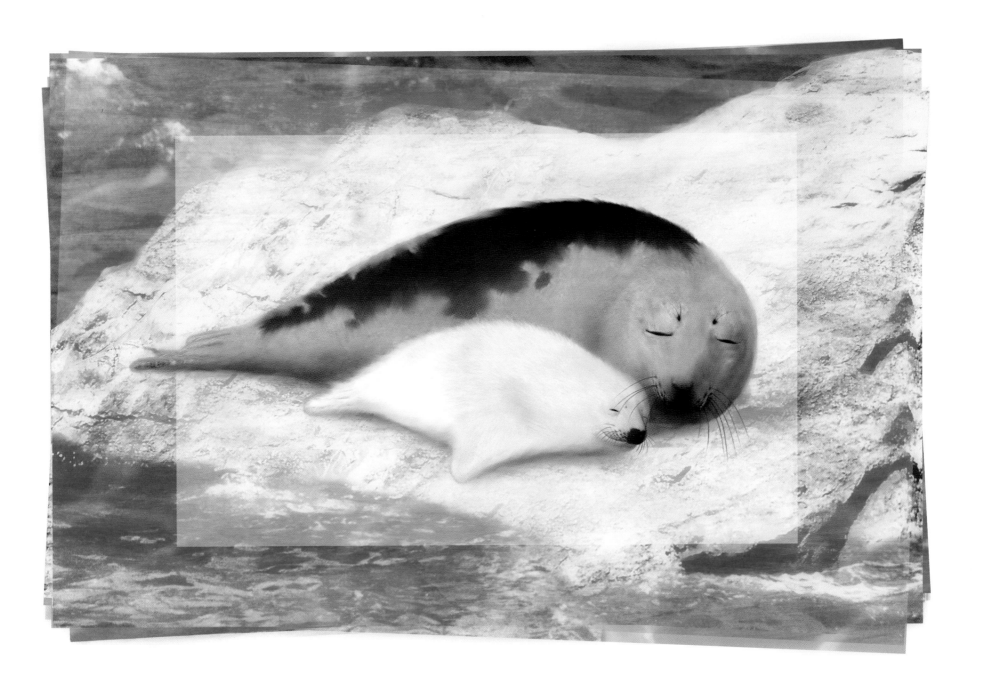

Mama Seal keeps Little Pup warm as they both settle down for the night.

Early the next morning, it's Little Pup who wakes up first.

Uh, oh! Look who's hiding in a bucket of fish. Now you see him…

And now you don't.

He's a pup on the run, making mischief all over the park.
Where can that curious seal pup be?

Mama Seal wakes up worried. She barks for help.
"Shamu! Can you help find Little Pup?"

I'm a whale who likes to help.
I'll ask my friends to look here, there, and everywhere.

First I'll ask the dolphin family. I like them a lot. "Have you seen Little Pup?"

"We'll search Dolphin Cove and let you know," answer the friendly dolphins.

The dolphins look up. The dolphins look down. The dolphins look all around.

"We can't find Little Pup, Shamu. Why don't you ask the manatee?"

The big, lovable manatee swims left and right. "Nobody here but me!" he says.

The polar bear jumps in the water and out again.
That bear splashes everywhere. But he can't find our friend, either.

The penguins waddle back and forth across the ice.

"We're keeping our eyes open for Little Pup. But none of us can see him."

"We haven't seen that slippery seal either," say the beluga whales.
They look near and far.

The playful sea lions are not quiet – they're the loudest lookers of all.
"We're looking left and right," they bark. "Sorry, Shamu!"

"No seal here," snap the sharks. "But we'd be very happy to help you find him."
No thank you, sharks!

Even the big turtle tries to find the little seal.
She stretches her neck and slowly swims in circles.

Poor Mama Seal looks high and low. Like any mama,
she's sad and worried when her little one goes wandering.

My dolphin friend has an idea.
"Shamu! You're the highest jumper. Jump up and look across the park."

That's a great idea! I take a big jump. I take a big look.

And I make a big...wet... SHAMU SPLASH!

And a wet, wet Little Pup wakes up.
He was sleeping right next to Mama the whole time.

It was just a little seal dream.

Don't look now, but guess who just found a bucket of fish?

Oh, no! Here we go again!

Learn all about the animals in this book!

~ **Killer Whales**, like Shamu, are large black-and-white mammals. They weigh a lot (between 3,000 and 12,000 pounds), and can grow up to 33 feet long.

~ **Harp Seals** live where it is very cold. Baby harp seals have white fur until they are 2 to 3 weeks old to help them hide in the snow. After that, they lose their fur and are gray and black in color.

~ **Dolphins** are mammals that live in warm oceans all over the world and are usually gray and white in color. They are smart, swim very fast and can hear things twice as far away as people can.

~ **Manatees** have two flippers and a tail that is shaped like a paddle. They are about 10 feet long and are peaceful, playful animals that only eat plants. Because there are not as many manatees as there used to be, they are called "endangered."

~ **Polar Bears** live in the Arctic, which is very cold and near the North Pole. Even though they look cute and cuddly, they can be very dangerous. They are the largest meat-eaters in the world and have paws 12 inches wide!

~ **Penguins** are birds that have feathers and wings, but cannot fly. They live by the sea, so they spend a lot of their time swimming and looking for food. They have webbed feet that help them in the water and also make them stand straight up on land.

~ **Beluga Whales** are white in color and live in the ice-cold waters of the Arctic. Their bodies are fat and blubbery to help them stay warm. They have no fin on their backs like other whales do, so they can swim right under the ice and find places to breathe.

~ **Sea Lions** are a kind of seal that live in the Pacific Ocean. They are different from other seals because they have ears on the outside of their heads like people do.

~ **Sharks** are fish, not mammals, so they have gills and can breathe underwater. There are many sizes of sharks, from the 10-inch long midwater shark to the 45-foot long whale shark. All sharks have many rows of teeth and five different kinds of fins.

~ **Sea Turtles** have large shells just like land turtles do, but cannot hide their head or legs inside. They can be green, yellow, brown or black in color, and are very good swimmers and divers. The only time they come on land is when females lay eggs. Males spend their entire lives in the ocean.

Did you find Little Pup? A harp seal pup was hidden near the SeaWorld lighthouse, in Dolphin Cove, and with the penguins, beluga whales, and the sea turtle.